# SONGS
# PO

**OTHER POGO BOOKS** *Pogo • I Go Pogo • Pogo Peek-A-Book*
*The Pogo Sunday Book • The Pogo Stepmother Goose • The Incompleat Pogo*
*Uncle Pogo So-So Stories • Potluck Pogo • The Pogo Papers • The Pogo Party*

**SIMON AND SCHUSTER • NEW YORK • 1956**

# OF THE
# GO

by **WALT KELLY** with
**NORMAN MONATH** at the clavichord

All the music in this book is original and published for the first time, except for the melodies to the songs "Deck Us All with Boston Charlie" and "Wry Song," the piano arrangements of which, however, are original. Any arrangement or adaptation of the compositions in this book without the consent of the owner is an infringement of copyright.

FIRST PRINTING

LIBRARY OF CONGRESS CATALOG CARD NUMBER: M56-1011

MANUFACTURED IN THE UNITED STATES OF AMERICA

LITHOGRAPHED BY COLORGRAPHIC COMPANY, INC., NEW YORK

BOUND BY H. WOLFF BOOK MANUFACTURING CO., NEW YORK

This is a book which probably should be "dedicated" (if that is the word) to a great many people whom we love and who have been helpful, or to a large number whom we love and who have not been helpful at all, except that they love us back in their particular blind persistency. However, if all of these will forgive us, perhaps we can point out that in many ways this is Kathryn Barbara's first look at the Christmas tree and she would like very much to share it with a little girl named Ruth Doris.

WALT KELLY

# CONTENTS

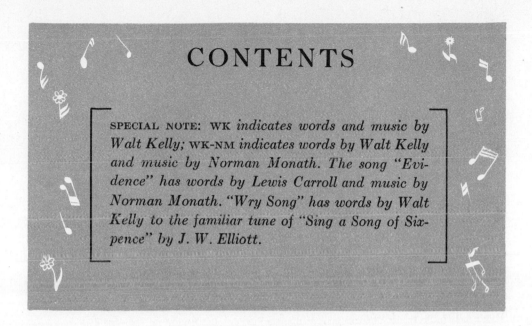

SPECIAL NOTE: WK *indicates words and music by Walt Kelly;* WK-NM *indicates words by Walt Kelly and music by Norman Monath. The song "Evidence" has words by Lewis Carroll and music by Norman Monath. "Wry Song" has words by Walt Kelly to the familiar tune of "Sing a Song of Sixpence" by J. W. Elliott.*

# A FOREGOING CONCLUSION

THERE IS little to be said about the words to be found in this book, and nothing is going to prevent it from being said at great length. Most of the words speak for themselves like magpies, with more shrillness than clarity and with a firmness born of a relentless lack of aim. This much can be said for not aiming at anything in particular: you later can circle the thing hit and call it the target, for no one is ever sure what you were shooting at. There are always willing bystanders who pluck straws from the wind of their mouths long enough to give you credit for a bull's-eye which you have never held in your sights. Thus, with stealth, and the help of the wise, a man may build a reputation which will bring him honor and also completely unhorse him when he finally tries to send a lance against the expected in the full light of day.

So, most of the words here should be viewed with a light eye. They are the sort of noises you should make when you jump over a brook in the springtime. They are the noises made by a child's toy rolling downstairs; the noises made by a determined grandfather eating corn on the cob. They are the nostalgic noises made by the squealing of a 1921-22 radio (if you listen closely you may hear KDKA now). They are the new noises that frog-peepers put out in the April evening. They are also the noises made in the winter of our discontent as we await the March trade winds and the hopeful breeze of a new baseball season.

Not all of the words are to be eyed lightly, however. The Rev. Charles Dodgson, known to everyone as Lewis Carroll, laid row after row of words like square-cut bricks when he fashioned the verse quoted by the White Rabbit in *Alice in Wonderland*. Inasmuch as the walls still stand and the roof still arches, it has been pleasant from time to time to crawl into the cool shadows of the edifice over the past few years and to look out of the windows. The Lewis Carroll book, and especially the scene of the Trial of the Knave of Hearts, remains even today a structure cut whole clay out of the world around it. To paraphrase an observation made by a four-year-old boy, it is also one of the few houses ever to have been built out-of-doors.

So, viewing it with such obvious covetness, there has been no alternative except to swipe part of it again. The result will be found set to music by Norman Monath (with small help from Kelly) in the Gold Room down the corridor, which you will recognize by the sound of singing hovering around its doorway.

There was an editor who in listening to the plan for this book assumed a worried expression and said, "Whoever writes the music must somehow be able to get the full sense of the words." This was a little quaint, inasmuch as the man who wrote the words never seemed to have had a two-handed hold on the sense of them. However it does appear now as if Norman Monath, who wrote much the best part of the music, has gracefully either discovered a sense here or added one.

A writer of words, like a cartoonist, is a fuss-budget about his work. He feels like a she-bear feels toward her cubs, suspecting that in any other person's care the perfection, the exquisite delicacy of the offspring will somehow be perverted and the months of nurture, the hours of labor, will go for naught as the fruit of the loin blossoms into a full-blown monster. Perhaps a she-bear is justified in this because most baby bears under their mother's guidance grow into generally recognizable replicas of their parents, which is what the bears seem to have in mind, although to some it may seem like an ill-advised plan. No trial of having a bear cub raised by a kangeroo is on record, so we do not really know what the experiment might yield.

The father of the words then also has a protective concern. He counts the little words at night and caresses them by day, tries to keep them in their proper order and bristles at strangers who either do not understand his words or imply that their words can lick his words.

With some misgivings, the verses found in either the daily POGO strips since 1948 or in the POGO books from 1953 on were gleaned, washed, buttoned into their little jackets, and with new haircombs and lunches sent on their way to Mr. Monath with many instructions about not only how *they* should behave, but how Mr. Monath should behave. They were told how to handle themselves in the event that the music master tried to start anything.

These suspicious overtures proved to be entirely unnecessary, for Norman Monath has gotten things out of the words which they did not know they had in him. He threw away about five-sixths of the musical trick plays which their father had painstakingly ground into their form of attack and has molded a hard-hitting team which may go through the season undefeated.

Certainly Norman Monath's general sensitivity even to the waves of sense which may not be there has created some haunting and lovely music. He has been a great working companion although he did throw out some very valuable suggestions by the author which had always worked for Rimski-Korsakov.

A few of these tunes have been picked out on a child's xylophone by the greatest one-finger virtuoso of the age, but the bulk of the work bears the stamp of Norman's gift for combining one man's verse with another man's music. Therefore, here is a rising, heartfelt vote of thanks from the characters of a comic strip to Norman Monath.

Always lurking in the background of any great tragedy there is the shadowy figure of a woman. In this case it is Miss Helen Barrow, a lively young lady who has at least two of the handsomest brown eyes in the looking business. Only because she has kept one of these eyes on Kelly and the other on Monath has this book ever been finally put together. Miss Barrow operates in the tense depths of the production department at Simon and Schuster, and it has been her quick calls for scalpel, sutures and plasma which have made at least one patient ambulatory enough to get around on its own. This book, which is as much hers as anybody's, is that result. Hum a little soft music, professor, we are dying like flies.

WALT KELLY, *September 1956*

# Go Go Pogo

A LITTLE LESS than a century before this writing, a determined group of backwoodsmen gathered together in one of our frontier states and eyed a tall, lean, gangling fellow. "He looks okay to us," said one, using a new expression. With this the men sent through their petition: THIS was the man they wanted for president.

One of the group was a traveling musician and entertainer who had written many a riverboat jig. "What we need is a campaign song," he declared, and he sat down at the piano and wrote the song we see here on the next pages. To the tune of the new song the frontiersmen swarmed onto one of the big Mississippi River boats and set out for the capitol. They were confident that the man who was one of them, the man whom they carried on their shoulders and in their hearts, would be the next president.

When Piedmont F. Pogo and his followers arrived in Washington they found the country already had a president. "What do you want HIM for?" asked the campaign manager for the frontiersmen, speaking to an important passerby. "We've got the right candidate right here." And he pointed to Mr. P. F. Pogo, who stood seven feet tall and weighed upwards of 145 pounds. A memorable figure of a man. "Piedmont," said the campaign manager, "wrestle for the man." And Piedmont put on a show of wrestling before the bystander which impressed anyone whoever saw it. Piedmont wrestled only himself. He lost. But it was close.

"Well," said the man, "he looks all right, but like I say, we've got a president. 'Nother thing. It ain't a presidential year. You can only get elected when there's an election."

"Is that a fact?" exclaimed the C.M.

"Fact," said the man. "'Nother thing. You going to have a candidate . . . you going to have a party. Can't have one without thother."

"Is that a fact?" exclaimed the C.M.

"Fact!" said the stranger, and bid them all a pleasant good morning.

"Fellows," cried the campaign manager, "how much money we got?"

The crowd dug up about forty-two dollars which they put in the manager's hat. He counted it slowly and then said, "If we gotta have a party, we *got* to have a party."

The party, at one of the smaller inns, turned into quite an affair, at which the police finally presided. The frontiersmen, several months later, returned home, footsore and pale. It was the end of Piedmont's political career. When he was asked later if he'd like to return to Washington, he replied that no, he'd seen it.

The song to which his friends rallied, even in later years, is printed here in its original version.

# GO GO POGO

Land a-live a band o' jive will blow go Po-go,

I go you go who go to go pol-ly voo go, From

Car-a-van Di-e-go, Wa-co and Os-we-go,

**f**

Wheel-ing, West Vir-gin-ia, With ev-'ry-thing that's in ya,

**mp** _____ **mf** **rit.**

Down the line you'll see the shine from Or-e-gon to Car-o-line, Oh,

**a tempo**

een-ie meen-ie min-ie Ko-ko-mo go Po-go.

**a tempo**

18

Tish - i - ming - o, sing those ling - o, whist - ling go. Sha -

mo - kin to Ho - bo - ken, Chen - ang - o to Chic - ong - o, it's

gol - ly, I go goo goo go - in' go go Po - go. As go go Po - go.

*8*

PATTER
*mp* (spoken)

The part-y of the first part and the part-y of the

no Pedal

next Were part-ly part-i-cipl-ed in a sparse-ly cov-ered

*accelerando e crescendo poco a poco*

text. Were you part-ial to a part-y that has par-celed out its

*accelerando e crescendo poco a poco*

parts To a fact-ion that was sec-ond in your par-ley-tick-le

heart? Then par-lay all your los-ings on a horse that's run-ning

dark. With lights out you may trip-le in a hom-er in the park! As

*D.S. al Fine*

# *A Song Not for Now*

THERE IS NOT much that should be said about this song, involving, as it does, the name of a lady. This much can be said in response to repeated questions from authorities (civil and uncivil): it means exactly what it seems to say and that is as surprising to those of us here at Bonny View* as it is to everybody else.

---

*Visitors twice weekly. Women, Wed. and Fri.; Men, Mon. and Sat.

# A Song Not for Now

Slowly, with expression

A song not for Now you need not put stay, A

tune for the Was can be sung for to - day, The

notes for the Does-not will sound as the Does, To-

day you can sing for the Will-be that was.

24

# Don't Sugar Me

To COMPLETELY understand the emotional storms and stress that resulted in this bit of truly heroic music it is necessary to go all the way back to the dawn of our American History, to a time when Miles Standish, John Alden and Priscilla Blotchkiss staged the Boston Tea Party.

It is necessary to go back to the top of the lonely church tower where Paul Revere waited, one hand on the rein, one foot in the stirrup, ready to ride throughout the length and breadth of this great land of ours warning the people that the British had set fire to Washington, which everyone will now admit was an insult to the first President of the United States.

The Tea Party so carefully planned by Priscilla Hogarrty had no sooner started on the decks of the good ship *Lexington* than British sailors disguised as Indians swarmed up the yard sheets and over the mizzen rails, swooped down upon Standish and Alden, who were making sandwiches of bread and butter, and threw those two worthies overboard. Each time the men would bob to the surface the Indians would pour tea down upon the pair. This was intolerable and, in fact, quite revolutionary because the tea contained cream and sugar.

Alden and Standish made their sticky way ashore and immediately levied a tax on Indians.

It was at this point that Priscilla Overwood drove the British off with her bodkin, uttering a series of sharp cries. These cries, or yelps, were noted down by a ship's chandler and preserved in the log for posterity to see. We now see it here in all its savage strength.

# DON'T
# SUGAR ME

Saucily
*mf*

Oh,   I   may   be   your   dish   of   tea   But   ba - by   don't   you

*mf*

*with Pedal*

"Sug-ar" me! Don't stir me boy,____ Nor try to spoon.____

Don't sug ar me____ 'cause us is THROON____ Oh

*rit.* *a tempo*

I won't sip a lip with you, 'Less you want a gran-u-lat-ed

lump or two Just roll them eyes_____ Right out that door._____

*rit.*

_____ Them sauc-er eyes_____ ain't square no more._____

*mp a tempo*

All them things, them dia-mond rings, Them stuff you prom-ised

me Were Fig-ments, Newt-on, sure as shoot-in'.

Shoot-in' sure as A, B, see, The tea pot pouts that the

ket-tle's blue, It don't work out that Spout is true Just

boil a-way boy_____ Don't sit and brew._____ Don't

sug-ar me_____ 'cause us is THROON._____

# Whither the Starling

WE HAVE arrived at that stage of our development when man's greatest enemy threatens to become or already is the STARLING. With great ingenuity we have recorded upon tape the painful notes of a starling in anguish, and when this is played to an itinerant starling he recoils like a brother-in-law presented with a snow shovel. With great compassion we thus force the starling to abscond with the bread crumbs laid out for the winter-bound robin. The problem is just this: Where do we drive the starling *to* when we sneak up behind him with a record machine which screams, in starling, "Help, Clarence, they have got me and they are smearing my head with ice cream"? If eventually everyone has one of these devices, we will have a lot of startled starlings hovering at about 20,000 feet, blotting out the sun and putting skywriters out of work.

There was a time when this danger was not present. A quaint song scraped off the bottom of a wheelbarrow found in a wet place in Virginia recalls to us the time when the Great Dismal Swamp was envisioned by many forward-looking pioneers as the future Venice of the U.S. A family of gondoliers was imported at the then truly high salary of $50,000 per diem to sort of row around the place and sing a little to test the acoustics as well as the wet-

ness. Unfortunately the group arrived in their new land without oars. Sent home again to correct this condition, they arrived back this time with the oars, but two had forgotten their mandolins and one had a severe head cold. This situation was no sooner remedied than the swamp dried up for three days. The promoters had already sunk well over $15,000,000 into the project in daily pay and lunches and refused to go any further. Disheartened and blue, the gondolier group returned to its native land to live in squalor.

While these hardy singers were in our land they were bothered continually by starlings. The starlings treated the Venetians as if they (the starlings) were mosquitos. The birds would settle in large flocks upon the unhappy singers, making their work both pizzicato and hazardous. The gondoliers made noises like Venetians in distress but this did not seem to affect the starlings in the least bit. Mosquito nets were of no use — sun-tan lotion helped a little but made the singers just a bit sick at their stomachs. Finally one, Benrus, exclaimed, in Venetian of course, "*Wither* them starlings!" This remark was expanded into the song which we note here.

It is claimed that the original song, in Venetian, had a different air and a much more colorful set of words.

# Whither the Starling

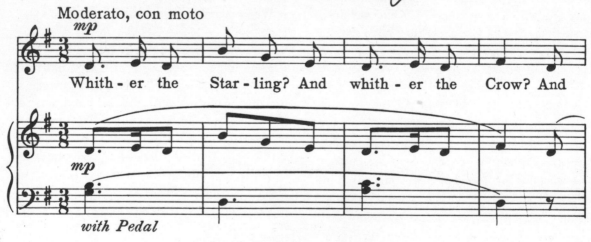

Moderato, con moto

Whith - er the Star - ling? And whith - er the Crow? And

with Pedal

whith - er the Weath - er when with - er the Snow? The weav - er's wet

Daught-er has damp-ened the clothes With wave-lets of wat-er left

# Whence That Wince?*

THIS IS essentially a ballad of love and jail, two elements that have produced some of the saddest music ever heard. When this ballad was first unearthed from a spot where primitive health authorities are rumored to have buried it, it was exhibited to the Mayor of Runigs, an outstanding authority on primitive music. "It is the saddest piece of music I have ever beheld," said the mayor.

Some have held that this song was one of the original "cave" songs. These, like cave paintings, have been discovered from time to time and sound best when played upon the ancient lithophone, one of which can be constructed easily in the back yard in one's spare time. A heavy maul or sledge-hammer is needed to strike rocks of various sizes. For example, eight round rocks ranging in size from a yard in diameter (for "C") on up to eight yards in diameter (for lower "C") are arranged in a simple, yet tasteful, row on the lawn behind the house. This instrument, of course, produces only one full octave, but friendly neighbors can easily be persuaded to expand their musical education and to have "real fun" at the same time. A block of five houses, for example, would yield almost enough room to have about one half of a piano keyboard. Certainly two blocks would about do it, especially if the police

could be convinced that shutting off the street intersecting would be an act of civic necessity and a cultural step forward. We have always found the police willing to co-operate in matters of this kind.†

The technique of playing the lithophone is similar to that of the xylophone but also like that of the piano. In other words, the hammers are actually better to work with if they are used as fingers. It would probably be impossible for the average man to carry five sledge-hammers in each hand and yet make a full run of the keyboard when a running crescendo of sixteenth-notes is called for. Personally we believe the player could achieve the same thing with only two mauls in each hand, and that would make the movement up the street for about two and a half blocks at a brisk pace more of a possibility.

About "Whence That Wince?" we will merely point out that this ancient lament is certainly an excellent piece to try the moment you can put your own little lithophone together.

---

*Or also widely known as "Ain't It Sad How the Bartender's Girl Friend's Momma Is in the Pokey?" Either title, of course, is quite appropriate.

---

†Mordid V. Querls, the eminent critic, has pointed out that if a stone eight yards in diameter is the "C" below middle "C" then the stones for notes down to the last key on the keyboard would be progressively and proportionately larger. This may be true and would mean that one should keep his eye open for good round rocks ranging in size up to eighty-eight yards across. A walk along any beach during the summer "fun" months would probably reveal a lot of possibilities. Care should be exercised in selecting only those stones which have perfect pitch.

# Whence That Wince?

With gusto

I was stir-rin' up a stir-rup cup in a stol-en ster-ling stein, When I

chanced up-on a lad-le who was once my Val-en-tine. "Oh,

36

whence that wince, my wench?" quoth I; She blushed and said, "Oh, sir, old dad-dy is-n't stir-rin' since my mom-ma's been in stir."

# The Keen and the Quing

DURING the days of the last century, when so many experiments in communal living were made, when different philosophies of society were given free rein in communities throughout Our Land, a bold bid to retain the Royal rather than foster the Common way of life was made by Zanias Tattersal.

Tattersal was the son of T. MacOttawa III, who had bought the state of Michigan, much of Indiana, two-thirds of Illinois, a controlling interest in the Mississippi River and, for some reason, half of Nicaragua. (A bridge was to be built between the holdings so that MacOttawa might not have to set foot on foreign soil.) MacOttawa called himself King of The Lands. He had made the purchase from a traveling tinker who, showing him bills of sale and grants from Emperors and heads of state in foreign lands, had proved that these areas were rightfully his (the tinker's). MacOttawa, in turn, handed over ten dollars in cash, his claim to Rhode Island, and a wagon wheel in excellent condition.

Upon his deathbed MacOttawa assigned his rights in all his holdings over to his son, Zanias Tattersal.* His son immediately set out on a trip to collect taxes and to distribute largess (in case he collected enough in taxes) and to test the simple friendliness of his subjects.

The simple friendliness of his subjects was put to a severe test at the first town, Elkhart, where young Zanias stopped. He gave his name to the town clerk, who looked at him blankly when Tattersal went on to demand a look at the town's books and a small advance on taxes to be collected the next year. He was hustled out of town a brokenhearted man. Then he realized that what he had to do perhaps was distribute largess immediately so that he would be recognized.

Tattersal collected himself a bushel basket of largess from a neighboring field and stopped in at the farmhouse next door, where the lady of the house set the dogs upon him and called him a thief. "I watched you stealing them tomatoes," cried the woman, a Mrs. Frugal T. Davis. Tattersal did not deign to point out that he had collected them as a gift for her and retreated rapidly and sadly. He was stopped at the town limits by a policeman who charged him with stealing a dog, and it was a fact that a small fox terrier was still attached to Tattersal's trousers.

Thoroughly disillusioned, Zanias realized that the country was not ready for royalty. He thereupon persuaded a group he met upon the road to start a royal community where everybody would be a king. In this way he hoped to have the movement spread. He wrote a song which was to be played by a thousand-piece band during the lawn-tennis hours, but the kings were run off so many village greens that they soon grew tired. Some men in helmets also appeared before long and took Zanias' new friends back to someplace from whence they had come. All that poor Tattersal could claim as his kingdom was the song he had written, and he traded that to a Mr. K. Highet for a can of evaporated milk. We have sent Mr. Highet a can in return and we print the words and music here. Zanias later made money in tatting.

---

*Tattersal was so named because his mother was fond of the sound. She hated MacOttawa as a name and, in fact, hated MacOttawa.

# The Keen and the Quing

**Liltingly**
*mp*

1. The Keen and the Quing were quirl-ing at quoits in the
2. (Now vi - ol - in on - ly with piz - zi - cat - to) plink-ey

*mp*

*with Pedal*

mead-ow be - hind of the mere,____ Tho' main-ly the mead-ow was
plink-ey pa - lunk-it - y plank ____ Pa - lunk-y pa - lunk-y plink

mid - dled with mow, an her - et - i - cal hith - er - to here._____ The
plink plink plink plink (ar-co) zoo-oo-oom zoom-it - y zoom. Ska-

Prince and the Princ-ess were plait - ing the plates and prat - ing quite
week - it - y squea-ky squeak squeak-y ska - week (con - sor - di - no)

prim-ly the Peer,___ And that's why the Duch-ess stuck ducks on the
squeak-y ska - week,___ (Now sen - za sor - di - no) squeak squeak squeeek-

*rit.* *a tempo*

1. *molto rit. e dim.*  2. *molto rit. e dim.*

Duke for . no one was ov - er to seer.___ Now
eek (Now piz - zi - cat - to) plunk plunk      plun —— k.

*rit.* *a tempo*

*molto rit. e dim.*   *molto rit. e dim.*

# Parsnoops

MILADY BRUHARROW collected this old fragment of song while conducting a paper drive for the Innswick Bugle and Viola Corps, a fine amateur group of volunteers dedicated to cheering the ill and consoling the bereaved.

"We was collecting a garbage wagon full of old papers to sell for what we could get so we could buy one of them what do you callems for the conductor," said Milady in a recorded interview made by a field worker. "No, I don't mean a ticket punch, not that kind of conductor. This conductor of ours was the fella what stands up in front of the orchester and waves his arms and keeps birds and bugs away so the fellas can play good on them hot summer nights when a body can't sleep.

"I remember like it was yesterday, actually it was Tuesday last, Mr. Wm. Harrygs, the butcher over on Elm, come out and said, how about coming in and helping me carry out the stuff, so I for one said I didn't mind. Well, nobody else spoke up. So *I* says, I says, Mr. Wm. Harrygs has said that he has this here bunch of papers and all inside and would we go in, I says. Well, nobody stirred. I says, it's a pity, I says, Mr. Wm. Harrygs, that nobody here got much ambition, I says, and furthermore, I think it's a shame, I says. Well, Merna speaks up and says, she says, if anybody wants to go inside his house they can, she says, and I says, well, I says, that ain't really no way to talk, I says, after all Mr. Wm. Harrygs has been a pillar of this town, I says, and has been saving paper like he was asked, I says, which, I says, is more than some people I know, I says. Because Merna, you know, never saved nothing and furthermore, mark my words, she never gave nothing away, even if it was dead, which you can't say about Mr. Wm. Harrygs.

"Merna gets real sore then, she says, WELL, MISS BRUHARROW, if you must know, I have counterbuted to the drive a rare old print of a poem all framed and all, which will undoubtally bring more, she says, than all the old paper you collected, she says. Mr. Wm. Harrygs, who was at that particular time acting like a gentleman, I must admit, standing there quiet and picking his teeth behind his hand, not sucking them or anything, you know, just pleasant, he says, come on in, girls, I got some new-made dandelion wine and I just closed the shop and I'd be proud to have you try it. I says, come on, Merna, you might not get another chance at your age to taste dandelion wine, and right then Merna pulled this framed thing out from under the seat and hit me on the corner of my head sort of, and she says, you are a cheap garbage picker, she says, and I don't know what all, because my eye was ballooning up and Mr. Wm. Harrygs said, you better come in and let me put a steak on that eye, he says. So I let him help me in, and I was crying and screaming a little, and Merna was having trouble with the horse which didn't like screams, I guess. Anyways she didn't come in which if she was a REAL friend of mine she would of, but anyways, in we went and Mr. Wm. Harrygs tied this piece of meat over BOTH my eyes and he says there, there, he says, don't cry, and first thing you know he must of sneaked up, cause he says, don't faint, and puts a arm around my middle and pecks me on the cheek. WELL, I got one eye free and run out of there, and Merna says, I knew it, she says, and helps me back onto the wagon and off we went cause the horse wanted to go anyways. Merna and me made up and she gave me the poem and said she thought it was written by somebody famous maybe Geo. Washington or one of them. It's the same as this song here.

"Merna says after, I thought he was going to put steak on the eye, she says, that looks like a piece of chuck. We were going to give it to the dog but it made a nice sandwich."

# PARSNOOPS

Vivace
*mp*

Oh, the par-snips were snip-ping their snap-pers, While the

*non legato*

*mp*

no Pedal

pars-ley was parce-ling the peas, And par-sing a sen-tence from

hand - le to hand was a hor-net who hummed with the bees. The

tur - nips were pas - sing the time of the day in the

# Truly True

SIR HEDLEY KOW, writing a treatise on cakes and cookies in a cook book entitled "Hogmanay," mentions the story of Rumpelstiltskin and describes how on a visit to Ireland in early pre-Irish days one of the Gigantes tribe came upon a woman, two feet high, who called herself Girle Guairle.

This woman, actually a fairy, was skilled in the art of spinning and weaving, and on a wager with a princess or queen would offer to spin cloth of gold.

The nine-foot-tall Gigantes tribesman, named Gwydion, was believed to be an incarnation of an old pig-god, and having recently fashioned the Milky Way while tracking somebody or other he had been preoccupied by tales of the woman who could weave so well. Accordingly, when he discovered her in Ireland, he disguised himself as a princess, inasmuch as the little woman was disguised as a prince. Gwydion offered his (or her) hand in marriage on condition that the little woman (or man) would weave him (or her) a cloth of gold.

Girle Guairle immediately said that she (or he) would, but that the Princess (or Gwydion) would have to guess her (or his) name.

When Girle arrived next morning Gwydion said, "How are you this morning, RUMPELSTILTSKIN?"

Girle immediately stamped a hole in the floor and escaped, for Girle was none other than Rumpelstiltskin in disguise. Gwydion, who had the ears of a Belgian Hare, had overheard Girle singing that very night as she (or he) wove the cloth in a vale of Tralee. The song, a cryptic cryptograph containing a cryptonym, was bitten into the cloth of gold by Gwydion, who had nothing else to do that afternoon, and was thus preserved. The words are printed here, but the cloth of gold disappeared and is believed to have been later melted down for dental purposes (Gwydion's).

# TRULY TRUE

Tempo di Valse

*mp*

Gamb-o-ling on the gumb-o——— with the gam-bits

*mp*

*with Pedal*

all in gear,____ I daffed up-on a dil-ly____ who would

be my dol-ly dear.____ Oh, Dil-ly, I would dal-ly____

# *How Low Is the Lowing Herd**

IT IS NOT generally known, or better, is not generally admitted, that sheep are constant chatterboxes, speaking to themselves in such high-pitched voices that their conversations can only be heard by a tall dog.† On the wind-swept prairies where we herd most of our sheep, the jolly shepherd, astride his strong pony, needs a dog constantly at his side listening. It is good for a shepherd to know what his sheep are thinking.

Many songs have been written about dogs; one of the very best will be found elsewhere in this collection. The song given here which starts, "Do you herd sheep?" is in a way a tribute to the dog who reports to his master what the sheep are up to.

As everyone knows, all dogs originally had blue eyes. They came from the north country and were generally known as bears. When man started herding sheep, he domesticated the bear and had a fine companion, not only good for watching sheep but good for listening to them.

The song "How Low Is the Lowing Herd" is actually a conversion from the original Eskimo, the tongue of men who today inhabit the lands first roamed by the dog, who, as we say, was at that time a bear.

Heard in the Eskimo language, it is difficult to understand how this song went, but it is not difficult to understand why. Today it is the feeling of most authorities that this modern English version of the song is more acceptable. Truthfully, the Eskimo song was about the traditional wedding gift of a skin of eel oil, a bit of symbolism not easily translated into our own terms. It could be argued that a similar song about the gift of a set of white wall tires to a bride might suffice. At least it would be as close as we might get.‡

*Or how *high*, for that matter?
† *The Canards of Canarsie*, by M. Caniff.

‡Most Eskimos will admit that it is hard to get close to eel oil at its best.

50

# How Low Is the Lowing Herd

RECITATIVO
*mp meekly*                                                        *agitato*

"Do you herd sheep?"    old  gram - ma  sighed.    My

*mp meekly*                                                        *agitato*

*with Pedal*

*mf with resolution*

gram-pa leaped in fright.    "That gram-mar's wrong!" to me    he

*mf with resolution*

*f broadly*    *ff*

cried.    "HAVE you heard sheep?_____ is    right!"

*f broadly*    *ff*

# Slopposition

"FOR want of the shoe the nail was lost, for want of the nail the . . . , etc." is certainly as right as rain, to quote an old saying. The entire tenor* of the campaign in which Martin Van Buren lost out to the slugging sloganeering of William Henry Harrison's backers might have been changed had this particular song, "Slopposition," been delivered to Van Buren's headquarters when it was promised.

When "Old Tippecanoe" and his followers embarked on the campaign of insults, jeers, catcalls and other public promotions to defeat Mr. Van Buren, Martin immediately saw that the way to defeat these "scalawags" was to turn the other cheek. This he did for several weeks until one of his campaign managers pointed out that Martin was getting his brains knocked out. It is alleged that Mr. Van Buren did not for one moment hesitate when he saw that this was true. He immediately sat down and wrote a letter to a friend, Col. Pucely Poons, of Nome, Alaska, and requested that

*The entire tenor, as Fromage humorously points out, was actually completely "base."

Pucely write him a campaign song. He instructed that the song should be gentlemanly in every way and when his opponents saw the direction he was taking, they would "pull in their horns."

Some months after the letter was written Poons received it from a tired Indian runner and straightway sat down and wrote the friendly, trusting verses that we see here. He had some trouble with the rhyming, spelled "opposition" with two "m's" and took quite a while to persuade the Indian to run back down east. "It's down hill all the way," said the Col., and the Indian left.

Had he not been incorrectly advised at Seattle, the Indian would never have run by way of Mexico City. As it was, he did not make bad time. He arrived at his destination just as General Harrison was being inaugurated. The Indian, naturally mistaking the General for his patron, sang the song, in Chippewa, in a loud clear voice. The rest is history. Within forty days Tyler, the V.P., had ascended to the presidency.

# Slopposition

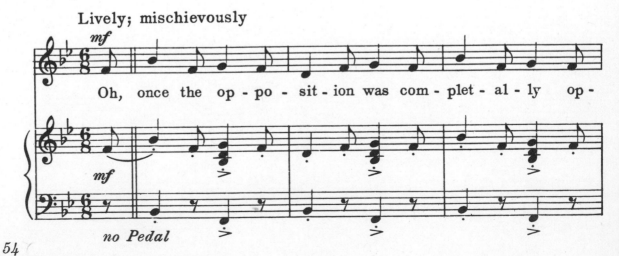

Lively; mischievously

Oh, once the op - po - sit - ion was com - plet - al - ly op -

posed To all the sup - po - si - tions that was

gen - 'ral - ly sup - posed; An' now the sup - er -

# Many Harry Returns

IT IS AT a mother's knee that one hears the songs of one's early youth. Their haunting melodies burn into the brain. No exception is the lullaby "Many Harry Returns." With this stirring tune riven into his consciousness as a small child, Major "Madman" Bunce Pundish remembered and sang it to his troops as they stormed Chicory Crossing.

Major Pundish was immediately slain, riddled by a hail of lead which observers believe came from both sides of the line. But he did not pass away until he had sung again the two verses we print here. His aide said that "all we could do was wait . . . it wouldn't of been fair to fire again."

The lullaby was then picked up by the enemy, who used it as a marching song. It is claimed that the song did more to win the war than ten regiments. Certain it is that as the enemy continued to use the melody their ranks became more and more split. At last a thoroughly disorganized rabble was put to flight, mumbling as they ran: " . . . 'fore one can be three be two; before be five be four!"

Old friends of Mrs. Pundish, Madman's mother, have conjectured that as young Bunce was dandled on his mother's knees he became confused as to words and tune. Mrs. Pundish was notorious throughout three counties as a woman of unusually squeaky knee caps. The squeaking of the knees plus little Bunce's own corduroy pants may have had some contributory effect on the tune and on the words as Major Pundish remembered them. Certain it is that the line "purple weather" had at one time a different meaning. Even the oldest inhabitants do not recall purple weather. Some have suggested that the line actually was "Inside of turtle's sweater."

This, of course, would make much more sense, but in the main we have found that it is best to stick to the traditions.

# MANY HARRY RETURNS

Andante, con moto

*mp*

Once you were two, dear birth-day friend, in spite of purp-le weath-er. But

now you are three and near the end as we grew-some to-geth-er. How

*with Pedal*

*dim.*

fourth-ful thou, for-sooth for you, For soon you will be more.— But 'fore one can be three be two; be-fore be five be four.—

# Evidence

IN THESE sunlit, civilized days when no man can be accused without facing his accuser, when he is presumed innocent until proven guilty, and when he is not required to testify against himself, it seems silly to think that our society was ever plagued by such a thing as a kangaroo court or by imperfect rules of justice.

We may laugh because we are secure now, but there was a time, many, many years ago, of course, when most people were predominately animals. One able historian, Lewis Carroll, has set down for us a court incident of a long-ago day. Evidence was presented in court by a White Rabbit which tended to convict a Knave of Hearts. As a result a ballad has come down through the years to us. The best introduction to the song is the court record left to us by Mr. Carroll, to wit:

*"There's more evidence to come yet, please your majesty,"* said the White Rabbit jumping up in a great hurry. *"This paper has just been picked up."*

*"What's in it?"* said the Queen.

*"I haven't opened it yet,"* said the White Rabbit, *"but it seems to be a letter, written by the prisoner to . . . to somebody."*

*"It must have been that,"* said the King, *"unless it was written to nobody, which isn't usual, you know."*

*"Who is it directed to?"* said one of the jurymen.

*"It isn't directed at all,"* said the White Rabbit.

*"In fact, there's nothing written on the outside."* He unfolded the paper as he spoke and added, *"It isn't a letter after all, it's a set of verses."*

*"Are they in the prisoner's handwriting?"* asked another of the jurymen.

*"No, they're not,"* said the White Rabbit, *"and that's the queerest thing about it."* (*The jury all looked puzzled.*)

*"He must have imitated somebody else's hand,"* said the King. (*The jury all brightened up again.*)

*"Please, your majesty,"* said the Knave, *"I didn't write it. They can't prove I did; there's no name signed at the end."*

*"If you didn't sign it,"* said the King, *"that only makes the matter worse. You must have meant some mischief or else you'd have signed your name like an honest man."* There was a general clapping of hands at this. It was the first really clever thing the King had said that day.

*"That proves his guilt,"* said the Queen.

*"It proves nothing of the sort,"* said Alice. *"Why, you don't even know what they're about!"*

*"Read them,"* said the King. The White Rabbit put on his spectacles.

*"Where shall I begin, please, your majesty?"* he asked.

*"Begin at the beginning,"* the King said gravely, *"and go on until you come to the end; then stop."**

---

*From *Alice's Adventures in Wonderland*, by Lewis Carroll.

EVIDENCE

Lively

*p*

They told me that you had been to her and men-tioned me to

*no Pedal*

gave him two, you gave us three or more._____ They

all__ re-turned from him to you, though they were mine be-

fore.\_\_\_\_\_ If I or she should chance to be in -

volved in this af - fair,\_\_\_\_ He trusts to you to

set them free ex - act - ly as we were._____ My.

no - tion was that you had been (be - fore she had this

fit)_____ An ob-stac-le that \_\_\_\_ came be-tween him,

and our-selves, and it._____ Don't let him know she

liked them best, for this must ev - er be ___ A

se - cret, kept from all the rest, be - tween your-self and me. ___ A

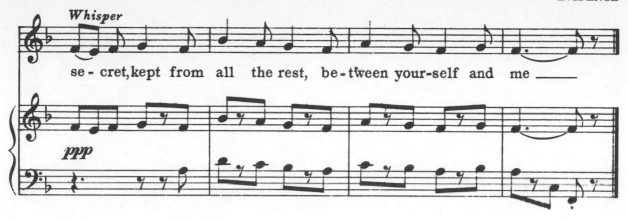

se - cret, kept from all the rest, be - tween your-self and me ____

# Lines Upon a Tranquil Brow

**T**HIS is the song of the old doormen, the ruddy-faced fellows whose breed is fast dying out. At the turn of the century it was a commonplace to hear this song, according to reliable reports. It was of this song that Cooper said, "When I first heard it I was speechless for eight months afterward."*

Mr. Cutlow C. Cutlow of Cutlow and Cutlow has supplied the words and tune used here. He gathered them on a visit to the old Punxatawney Club in Upper Black Eddy, Pa., during the winter of 1934. It will be recalled that the snow was unusually deep that year, and when Mr. Cutlow arrived there it was a bitterly cold night. Not many members had turned out and there was talk of footpads. In this eerie setting, then, Mr. Cutlow recalls that the door was kept closed most of the time. On a busier evening, or a warmer one, the door would have been swinging to and fro and frequent blasts of warm air from the cheery luxury of the club might have been warming the old doorman who stood outside.

*Reliable reports also report that Cooper was nearly ten months old when he first heard the melody. It was sung to him by A. G. Liadanoon, a child nurse, reportedly in love with the doorman formerly at Quilty's.

Mr. Craseagh Bimby arrived late, Mr. Cutlow says, and rushed inside with "a look of utter terror on his usually happy countenance." Bimby was given a brandy or two and after a spell said, "Something is out there." Accordingly, the door was barred and the two men and the bartender, F. Gulch, spent the night huddled before a roaring fire. Morning arrived, and seeing nothing from the windows, Mr. Cutlow ventured outside at approximately noon and saw on the sidewalk, frozen to the pavement, the cheerful form of the ruddy-faced doorman.

Taking time only for lunch and one short game of billiards, Mr. Cutlow and Mr. Bimby chipped the doorman free and slid him into the club. There they revived him and thawed him out with a candle. His first words when he awoke were "Where am I?" for he had never been in the club before. He was touched when his whereabouts were revealed. Out of gratitude, it may be assumed, he sang, just before they came to take him away, the song of his trade, the Doorman's Song. We can all be thankful that Mr. Cutlow was there with pencil and paper. His quick thinking preserved a real gem, a product of a simple, cheerful folk whose happiness hid much.

## Lines Upon a Tranquil Brow

**Liltingly**

Have you    ev - er, while    pond'- ring    the    ways    of    the

*with Pedal*

morn, thought to save just a bit, just a drop in the horn; To

pour in the ev'-ning or late aft-er-noon, Or dur-ing the

night when we're shin-ing the moon? Have you ev-er cried out while

count-ing the snow    or    watch-ing the tom-tit    warb-le Hel-

lo..."Break    out the cig-ars, this    life is for squirr'ls. We're

Ragtime

off    to    the drug-store    to    whist-le    at    girls".....?

# Mistress Flurry

IN THE TOWN of Bluebelfry it was generally admitted many years ago that Mistress Flurry was a witch. That is, it was generally admitted by everybody except Mistress Flurry. "She wouldn't admit it was Sunday on the day after Saturday," was the common remark. "She's a witch."

"Why don't you admit you are a witch?" travelers would ask her when they stopped by her simple cottage for a refreshing draft of cool milk. But Mistress Flurry kept her own counsel. If she was a witch she never let on, but continued to have a worried look, to rise early and predict rain and to throw salt over her left shoulder in a steady stream.

"Why do you throw so much salt over your left shoulder?" people would ask when they'd stop in for dinner. "It sometimes gets into the soup and into the corn fritters. It is a very bad habit. You always have hard luck, so what are you avoiding?"

"I throw it over my shoulder all the time because of the salt I've spilled by throwing it over my shoulder in the past. I spilled some salt in my early youth at the age of thirteen months. I've been at it constantly ever since. And as for avoiding hard luck, that is not my intent. I've become accustomed to the luck I've got. I don't want it to change. Who knows, it might get worse!" And she shuddered. "Who knows, it might get better!" She shuddered again.

Doctors and Savants were brought in, according to old accounts, to try to cure Mistress Flurry of her salt habit. "If we could only get her off the stuff," said the Mayor, Beer Bottome. "It's getting so that nothing grows behind her.

She salts everything. Nobody will sit behind her in church. If she sits in the front seat of a bus, it's a bad day for the bus company."

Eventually, as in most cases of this kind, the problem, by its very nature, solved itself. Mistress Flurry ran out of salt. She would scurry over to a neighbor's and borrow a pinch here and a pinch there. These she would quickly throw over her left shoulder and then, twitching, she would borrow, beg or sometimes, we are afraid, steal salt wherever she could. Before long the entire town of Bluebelfry was depleted of salt. Mistress Flurry was a quivering and pitiful case the day the circus came to town.

The circus parade moved up the avenue. Salt lovers in the circus retinue had been told that the town was dry, and many of them were in an ugly mood. The men in charge of the elephants were particularly disgruntled. Word had gotten around that Mistress Flurry was a witch. "She's a witch," was what they said.

When Mistress Flurry saw the newcomers, she unthinkingly asked one of the elephants for a pinch of salt. One of the handlers, thinking to play a prank upon the "witch," handed the poor woman a box of pepper. "It's almost the same thing," he said, with a leer. Mistress Flurry, walking dreamily ahead of the elephants, threw handful after handful of pepper over her left shoulder. You can imagine the result, of course. When the elephants were through with sneezing, Mistress Flurry was nowhere to be seen. And, in fact, she has never been heard from since that day. The only thing left is the song which children had delighted to sing at her, naturally keeping out of range.

# Mistress Flurry

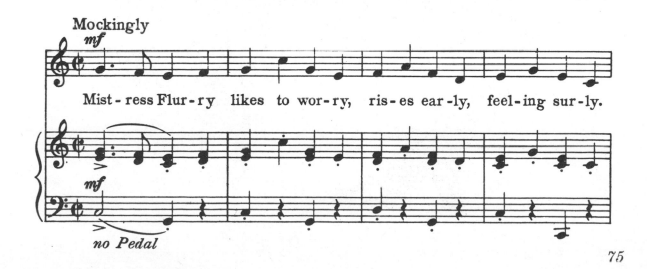

Mockingly
*mf*

Mist-ress Flur-ry likes to wor-ry, ris-es ear-ly, feel-ing sur-ly.

*mf*

*no Pedal*

There's no cure, for she is sure that life will be the

death of she. Best to wor-ry, Mist-ress Flur-ry.

# Man's Best Friend

WE ARE indebted to the Hon. Greenfield Hill for the following account describing the discovery and recording of the song known as "Man's Best Friend."

Mr. Hill writes:

> July 13
> "Hide-a-wee Cottage"
> Lake Mudge

DEAR TORRANCE:

Gladys and I arrived here on Monday noon. Found all in good order. Thks for suggestns. Will think them over. Always pays to think things over. Think that over. Gladys nearly drowned and has bad poison ivy. Warned her. Glad to report I am well. Brown as berry. Sleep late. Feeling tip top. Saw a scissortail flycatcher. Gladys said it was dove. City woman. Does not like all this cooking and wood chopping. Tell her it gives her something to do. I am busy with notes. Enclose notes on new song. At least never heard it before. Gladys says she has heard it. I tell her she has not. That's that. Gladys has always heard everything. Between you and me, I don't believe your sister was given even the normal share of Torrance brains.

Plumber came to collect bill for last year. Said you'd ordered something. What was it? It cost $45. I told him he could whistle for his $45. He took whatever it was away. Gladys tired of pumping water by hand. You ought to do something about it. She's your only sister. Old timer down the lake a ways was bitten by bad dog. Rabid. Seems he was singing enclosed. Dog suddenly went berserk. Bit him right through the guitar. I picked up the music when they carried him off.

As ever, HILL.

# MAN'S BEST FRIEND

Moderately, with sentiment

*mp*

What gent-ler eye,          What nob-ler heart

*mp*

*with Pedal*

Of be - lov - ed      Old Dog      Tray?

# The Prudent Promisor

SOME fast folkwork was necessary to finally round out the real story behind this simple, forthright, declamative song. We are indebted to Hathaway House for the account told here. The good, clean fun of the true "work song" shines through the spirit and indeed much of the true essence of this basic work, and Mr. House, in his memorable book, *Eggplant or Squash?*, tells how he came upon notes and words.

"I was traveling through lower Upper Darby," writes Mr. House, "by canoe in 1923. This may strike many of my friends as curious inasmuch as they know of, and approve, I venture, my fear of water in any form. This fear has long been a thorn in my side, as many, many of our best folk songs are not only ABOUT water but are often found near streams and other wet grounds, marshy places and, quite often as not, right at the very shores of our mighty oceans theirselves. Whether this is because the folk who live near water are more poetic or whether the water just plain causes a man or a lady, as the case may be, to just plain break into song is not plain. But the fact is that we find many of our most interesting work near open, or even closed, water.

"To get back to the reason why I was traveling by canoe through lower Upper Darby involves in itself an amusing sidelight to the work we collectors are engaged in. A friend, Mord Densey, was driving through that section of Pennsylvania in 1923 in a one-seater runabout borrowed from another friend, Mabel Nonce, with a folding top to which he had lashed a canoe to take to his cousin Geo. W. Densey, his father's brother's boy. He offered me a ride, as the scenery was pleasant at that time of year, except I would have to sit in the canoe and hold cousin Geo. W. Densey's dog, Homer, and chickens which he, Mord, was returning.

"This arrangement proved eminently satisfactory to me and Homer, a fine specimen of a brindle bull, but the chickens were clearly startled at the prospect and offered a steady show of resistance throughout the early part of the trip during which section on the road to upper Lower Darby, where we had to go first, we lost one chicken outright and another was bitten cruelly by the dog who became excited and as a consequence died. The chicken did, that is. Homer remained throughout the journey quite healthy.

"Our misfortunes started when the folding top collapsed upon Mord, sort of squashing him, muffling his screams and causing him total impairment of immediate vision. I shouted encouragement down to poor Densey, whose feet were jammed tightly down upon the gas pedal, and from time to time gave him instructions as we whipped along the highway at quite a brisk rate, occasionally going across fields and small streams. My own driving has never been of the best, and what with the awkward position atop Mord and holding the dog and several pullets, a broiler and a young rooster, I found myself quite busy and not in the best of form. As a consequence we lost Mord and the runabout when we negotiated several hundred yards of an old creek bed, which though completely dry was quite rocky and as a result of the rocks quite bumpy, I must say. We flashed under a very low bridge at one point, and the canoe and contents, which included the dog, Homer, the chickens, and me, were scraped off and Mord continued on his way at approximately one hundred miles per Hr., the top still jammed down upon him. We never did see Mord Densey again, although we got a postcard at Christmas time from Cleveland, a city in Ohio. It indicated that he was not a well man."

# The Prudent Promisor

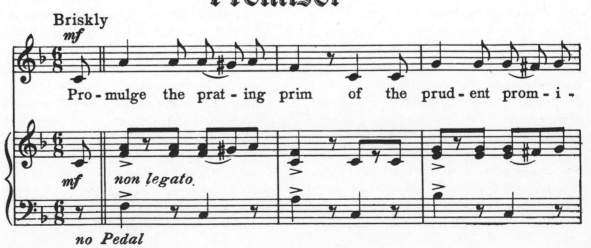

**Briskly**

Pro-mulge the prat-ing prim of the prud-ent prom-i-

*non legato.*

*no Pedal*

sor, For the prem-ise of the prom-ise was the prim-o-gen-i-

tor of the prim - a - lace - ous pro - gram with the

pres - by - op - ic door, Of the prim - a - lace - ous pro - gram with the

pres - by - op - ic door.

# Song of the Shuttle
## or
## Smile Wavering Wings

AN AIR known to spinners and weavers everywhere as "The Shuttle Song" is also known as the "Song of the Shuttle." It is the only verse or piece of music in the western hemisphere that is geared to go forward or backward at a moment's notice, or even at the same time.

It makes a jolly reminder of the days when grandmother could be seen spinning down in the cellar and grandfather weaved amongst the portieres in the upper hall. Grandmother in all probability would sing the song forward while Grandfather would sing it backward or both at once. This to the music of the shuttle and the loom made for merry evenings, and I am sure that we all miss those days of cracking nuts and ducking apples.

As you know, parlor music was very popular in olden times and many clever little stunts were performed upon the harpsichord and harmonium. Ander Flainwhinny has recalled for us the time when his father would perform music at the harpsichord upside down. The elder Flainwhinny spent a good deal of his life upside down and invented amongst other things the Upside-Down Haggis and the Reversible Cuspidor. Old Flainwhinny was able to perform the music upside down by either (A) being upside down himself; (B) turning the music upside down; or (C) turning the harpsichord upside down. Ofttimes he did all three at once. This latter trick was not so well received inasmuch as it was pointed out that except for position everything was just like it was in the first place.*

---

*"He was just trying to be smart. There was really nothing to it." — Mrs. A. Flainwhinny, Sr., in *Them Days*.

# SMILE WAVERING WINGS

Flowing

Smile, wa-ver-ing wings, a - bove rains pour__ While hope-ful-ly

*no Pedal*

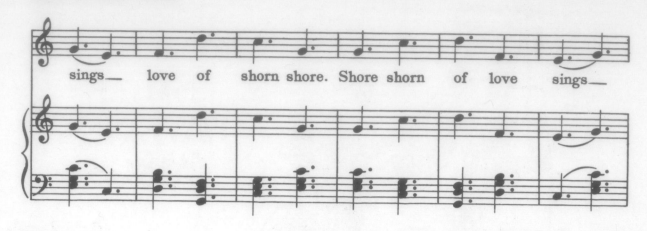

sings— love of shorn shore. Shore shorn of love sings—

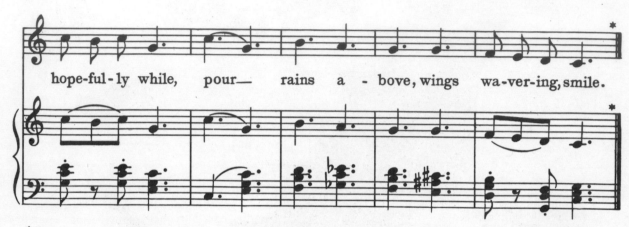

hope-ful-ly while, pour— rains a-bove, wings wa-ver-ing, smile.

* Repeat in reverse by reading notes right to left from end to beginning.

88

# Filibeg Fair

THE jolly noise of the country dance echoes up and down the valleys of one's memory as the strains of "Filibeg Fair" sound in any group. This lively air is just full of strains and the sharp-eared listener will get especial pleasure out of the juxtaposition of "on" and "the" directly preceding as they do the word "fringe."

One of the sharpest-eared of listeners was old Mother Roof, she who brought folk singing home to Ossining and who did so much to popularize the ratchet, the paper-covered comb and the two-story ladder. Her early students worked largely at night, and when they would return to the cozy comfort of the school in the early morning hours, carrying with them little gifts of gold-inlaid silverwear, mink coats, strong boxes, and occasional bundles of negotiable securities, their little eyes would just gleam at the sight of old Mother preparing for them a bowl of porridge and occasionally a real treat, hot water and sugar.

It was old Mother Roof who would bind the wounds made in their little trousers as they climbed in and out of windows and it was old

Mother Roof who taught them discipline. The warmth of her personality was burned into the students' little minds and she would rock them to sleep with a song on her lips every morning at eleven sharp. Usually the song was the rollicking, "There is Crepe Hanging Today on the Old Jail Door," but just as often, or even more usually, it was "FILIBEG FAIR." The children had great fun with old Mother as she would lose her teeth when singing this song and the little pranksters would often hide them.

Often the children would ask old Mother how she happened to be such a sharp-eared listener. But she would just laugh and lose her teeth. The true story seems to be that Mother Roof was once given a very short haircut by a whimsical barber in a sort of public institution. It was at this time that she acquired the affectionate nickname of "Rin Tin Tin."

We do not know where she picked up the song "Filibeg Fair," but we all owe thanks to Dersey's Pawn and Loan Emporium, where the manuscript was found tucked into Mother's effects.

# Filibeg Fair

With his Fil - i-beg Fair fil - i-greed with fin - est fil - i - form, He

fleet - ly foot - ed   froo an' fro   the   fig - wort in   the   storm.   A

flaught of Bor - e - al is and a fir - kin fine of fat, Was

fim - bri - ca - ted   on   the fringe of   Fre - ling-huy - sen's hat.

# Northern Lights

A REAL work song spawned by the simple folk of Westchester and the North Shore of Long Island is the robust "Northern Lights." Here is a tapestry into which is woven the entire fabric that was once the mantle of the garment.

Northern Light Watchers have always been a special group keeping at least one eye always pointed north throughout the deepness of the night. Over the centuries, as one of these lonely Watchers would sight the Aurora Borealis, he would rouse the town and turn people out of bed to witness the spectacle. Amateurs at the game have been known to send volunteer fire companies northward in search of burning barns at the sight of Northern Lights; therefore the more progressive sections have always had their little hardy bands of professional Northern Light Watchers.

This has always been a hard calling. For example, people in towns along the North Shore of Long Island have been known to complain at being turned out of bed. "It's only Stamford burning down," some might say, or again: "It is the Port Jefferson Ferry." Nonetheless, the Watchers have succeeded in establishing the fact that there are such things as real Northern Lights.

One New Jersey Watcher, Greyn Mentness, sighted in 1932 what he thought were Eastern, Southern, Midwestern and West Coast (Cal.) lights. He wrote four songs about this sight, but the songs were unfortunately lost in a saloon fire in Perth Amboy. Mr. Mentness was with them at the time.

The song used here is the one which became the working refrain of Northern Light Watchers everywhere. It came about when a young woman named Nora O'Roradoran discerned Northern Lights as she was waiting for her lover, Mr. Beans Borealis, to return from the delicatessen with a set of cold cuts.

Her balcony window overlooked a snowy driveway, and suddenly out at the end of the short roadway, against the horizon, there appeared a startling glow. It remained there for some time, and Missy Nora, as she was known by the simple folk of the village, heard the sound "Arora aurora–rora–rororora — aurora — rora — rora . . ." Straightway the quick-witted girl ran through the deserted streets and wakened the inhabitants. In small, huddled, respectful groups the people gathered on Nora's snow-covered lawn and watched the phenomenon. As they watched, one started singing softly the song we now know so well, "Oh, roar a roar for Nora/ Nora Alice in the night, etc., etc."

It later developed that Miss O'Roradoran's driveway pointed due south and the noise was caused by Borealis' car starter. He had stalled on his way back with the salami, bludwurst and kelbasi, and the starter produced the sound effect quoted above. The lights, of course, were his car lights, but we do not feel that these facts lessen the charm of the song one whit.

# NORTHERN LIGHTS

**Tenderly**

Oh, roar a roar for Nor - a, Nor-a A - lice

*with Pedal*

in the night,_____ For she has seen Aur-or-

a Bor-e-a - lis burn-ing bright._____ A

furioso

fur - ore for our Nor - a and ap - plaud Aur - or - a seen!

furioso

mp rit.      a tempo      dim.    pp

Where through-out the sum-mer has our Bor - e - a - lis been?____

mp rit.      a tempo      dim.    pp

# Lhude Sing Cuccu

IT HAS probably been the experience of every collector of folk songs or verse that often it is just one little clue, usually unrecognized by the untrained eye, which points the way to the treasure we seek.

The meaning of the words to "Lhude Sing Cuccu" has long been in doubt, although the music has been understood by most students. The tune, as many will remember, was described by Danning Fasly as a piece of music that took a man back.*

It was Professor Fasly and his wife, Pearl, who may well have uncovered the key to the riddle of "Lhude Sing Cuccu" while on a field trip in the Hebrides. The one little clue which this pair of keen-eyed observers noticed was a towering column of smoke rushing skyward on the western horizon. At the same time another column of smoke could be seen to the east. After some observation it was apparent that the smoke columns were being used as signals of one kind or another, and eventually Dr. Pearl, with her intimate knowledge of Blackfoot, was able to decipher the meaning of the signals. "It looks to me," said Dr. Pearl, "as if somebody is sending a humorous story from

*Fasly's very words were: "I was took aback."

the east there—and to the west; those short puffs indicate uncontrollable laughter." At this, Dr. Pearl related an amusing part of the story she had read in the smoke signals, which concerned several Scotch Indians named Pat, Mike and Begorra.

Later it was learned that Dr. Pearl had been somewhat in error, for the smoke, unfortunately, had been a sign that two towns several miles apart were afire and much property was destroyed. However, this does not entirely discount Fasly's theory that Dr. Pearl actually had stumbled on an important discovery. As Professor Fasly reconstructed it, the possibility is that in the early days barbarian children had developed the habit of sending and reading comic smoke signals.

These comic smoke signals in the errant air were no doubt open to some questionable interpretation. As a result, society invented the book, a more steady means of communication, and children were then able to read comic books without danger of setting fire to themselves or getting soot on their eyeglasses. It is believed that "Lhude Sing Cuccu" might have been a song written in celebration of the transition.

# LHUDE SING CUCCU

Resolutely

Och hwaer-so-c'er do nu we goe? An' whude we knaw't a do, Owre

child - er deore be faulne a - wa', whoum-ev-er shal ye sue? Coulde

we but tain they hand en own ere na they gan too farre, An'

*rit.*     *a tempo*

faest-en they on high raign-bogh ellse to yon spring-bryhte starre. Aye,

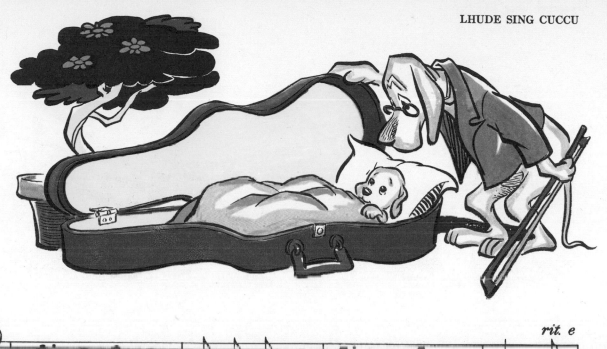

*rit. e*

whude we tain they pon y-knee for towlde they owt we knaw, Sic

*dim.*

*a tempo*
*mf*

they mought sweet the louve-ly-nesse en Tale on Longue-an-goe. Al-

lowe we now be fillt wi cayre on whyche bouke child-er reede, Ain

*rit. e dim.* **mp**

we shal na en fal-owe grunde, yet sow-eth owt owre seed.

*rit. e dim.* **mp**

# One Small Score for Two Brown Eyes

## or

## Only the Lone

SCRIBBLED on the flyleaf of the portfolio which contained this manuscript was the instruction, "Quick, my love, fetch the torch. There is no longer dark."

Exactly what Hevis II meant by this has long been a matter of conjecture. Only slightly less mysterious is the riddle of Hevis II himself. No one ever met him. That is, there are no reports. It is not even a matter of true record as to how exactly he spelled his name. Some claim that it originally had a capital Z, right in the middle. Others claim that this first group could not spell catt. Still others claim all the lands east of South Clark street in Chicago, and so it goes. *Who* Hevis II was, or even IF, remains unknown, but there is no denying the writing on the flyleaf, even though it was unsigned.

It is not known either whether Hevis II had a sister, Merl. It is believed that if there *was* one, there was just *one* of her or Merl I. Confusion has so far been pretty well avoided by calling her *plain Merl*. Some of those who have always believed in the legend of Merl's great beauty object to her being called *plain* Merl, but facts seem to indicate that she was not called very often anyway.

In the complete lack of claimants, students have attributed at least one verse to Merl. Again, lack of signature prevents us from truly knowing. It goes as follows:

> When I go in-to the wood,
> I see the lit-tle bun-nies,
> Eat-ing Por-ridge as they should!!
> Those cle-ver lit-tle rab-bits.

# ONLY
# THE
# LONE

Dreamily, not too slowly

*mp*

Eve-ning is dawn and night un-known, But here in the morn the

*mp*

*with Pedal*

104

mists are grown, And on-ly the loon will laugh a-lone, And

on-ly the lone are lorn;— And on-ly the lone are lorn.—

105

# Twirl, Twirl

BREATHES there the woman (or man) with ambition so dead who never to herself (or to himself) has said: "If I had but the time I should write a novel (or a book) or paint perhaps a painting or perchance write a wonderful sonata for the pianola (or bassoon, perhaps)"?

It is from longing such as this that great folk songs spring. Most folk songs are made up of notes and words and are sung through the nose, which is the quieter of our two vocal instruments. The nose has probably never been given the credit as a musical instrument which it so richly deserves. In folk music much is made of the role of the guitar, the mouth harp, the lyre, the drum, the bugle, the clarinet and the washboard, but scarcely ever do we hear much about the role of the nose.

A very fine effect can be achieved by anyone after only a few lessons upon the nose. It is not necessary actually to be able to read music, although it is true that some ability to carry a tune helps tremendously. There have been some instances of tone-deaf nose performers, but these monotones appear usually only at tobacco auctions and as train conductors or dispatchers. A few find itinerant work as air-raid sirens in small towns, but the need for sounding alerts has fallen off sharply and as Gesly Portance so quaintly puts it, "Pickin's are slim." Gesly alerted the entire town of Quincy Plain at a late hour one New Year's Eve, when a strange low flying object was identified as the mayor.

If the nose is held lightly, but firmly, between thumb and forefinger, it may be plucked rapidly, all the while humming, let us say, "Aloha" or "Howareya Tonight in Hawaiia?" or any other native chant. The proper technique, of course, is to make the plucking and the notes synchronize, producing a generally admirable effect.

Some performers are able after a few years of training to pluck the nose and hum and to whistle lightly between the teeth at the same time. There is not much demand for this, unfortunately.

The song in question here sprung from just such a folk player. It was Ollis Moody who sat idly plucking his nose at a performance outside the living room window of his sweetheart, Miss Goodoe. The soothing strains of "Aloha" had scarcely died away when Ollis embarked upon something which has come to be known as "Twirl, Twirl." Miss Goodoe was overcome and did not long retain the last name of Goodoe, you may be sure.*

So we can see that a piano or a bassoon is not necessary for composition. All that is needed is an idea and, as Mr. Moody wittily points out, "A nose for music."†

---

*Miss Goodoe married a Mr. Herman Snump of Elmira, North Dakota, the following December.
†Mr. Moody said that his inspiration for the song was a high-school dance.

# Twirl, Twirl

Lightly
*mp*

Twirl!     Twirl!     Twin-kle be - tween! The  tweez-ers are

*mp*

*no Pedal*

twist in the twit - ter-ing twain. Twirl! Twirl! En - twin-ing-ly

twirl 'twixt twice twen-ty twigs pass-ing plat-i-tudes plain.

Plun-der the plov-er and rov-er rides round. Ring all the

rungs on the bras-si - ly bound, Bil-ly, Swirl! Swirl!

Swing-ing-ly swirl! Sweep a-long swoop a-long sweet-ly your swain.

# Mistily Meandering

STUDENTS and musicologists have for years puzzled over the mystery of not only who wrote "Mistily Meandering" but who did not finish it. The music can be compared to the *Unfinished Symphony* of Schubert; that also is incomplete. However, in the case of Schubert, we know that it was HE who did not finish his work. In the case of "Mistily Meandering" there is a double problem. The question has often been asked but never answered, just WHO did not finish it? In this particular, we can easily see, then, the piece excels Schubert's *Eighth*; it is a far greater mystery. In addition, careful examination shows that it contains some of the very same notes.

Kidkins in 1956 offered the theory that the two works might be by the same man. He qualified this to the extent of saying that it was his belief that the unfinished portions had a great deal in common.*

His great rival Meersuckle immediately took issue and said that the unfinished part of the *Unfinished Symphony* is much longer than the unfinished portion of "Mistily Meandering." "There is also a distinct change in style," declared Meersuckle. "One glance at the MS silence that follows the ending of the *Unfinished Symphony* will convince a listener that he is about to listen to an entirely different kind of nothing than he hears when the song 'Mistily M.' comes to its untimely halt."

The question of who did not write the ending may never be settled, but painstaking research has begun to prove exactly who did not write any of the song. There are many claimants for this distinction and these men are being slowly and grimly interrogated. The process of elimination may one day reveal the answers to at least half our question; or half the answers to no question at all.

---

*"Both break off," said Kidkins. "Boop! Like that!"

# MISTILY MEANDERING

Dreamily

Mist-i-ly me-an-der-ing up-on a Mon-day morn,— I

maun-dered out to Man-da-lay where all the dawns are born.— The

chirp-ing of a Chick-a-dee who rode a Ron-de - lay,___ Re-

plete with wry - ly rue -ful rife up - on the *(overcome by sorrow)*

# This Is the Hunt

THERE WAS A TIME when most of us were rabbits or reasonable facsimiles with long cardboard ears, or were, at the very least, small jackasses. More clever men who had taken jobs as pigs, dogs, cats, wolves and even chickens would very often worry about us rabbits.

"Them rabbits, there," they'd say, pausing for effect and to give themselves time to think of the plural verb, "them rabbits are dangerous."

"Why?" asked a short-eared rabbit, whom everybody took to be an old coati-mundi. "Why?"

"Because they don't recognize danger like we do," said the pigs, dogs, cats, wolves, chickens, herons and foxes. "And anybody doesn't recognize danger like us is in danger of being swallowed up. You gotta be hep. You gotta be alert, and if the good Lord gives you two ears, one is for laying on the ground and listening with."

The rabbit put one ear to the ground and so the rest stepped on his head and left chuckling and giggling. "Them coati-mundis!" said one, which brought a good laugh.

So, the foxes and the pigs and the hippopotamuses and the elephants and the weasels and all, they kept a good watch on the rabbits because it was pretty clear that the rabbits would some day fall for the wiles of some real-estate salesman, be sold the center of the Atlantic Ocean, and in trying to reach it would all perish in the process.

One day an owl blew into town who announced that he had just struck water in Florida. Quickly he sold land to all the badgers, wolverines, beavers, lions, elks and dogs, and everybody left to enjoy the water. Everybody except the rabbits.

Nobody asked the rabbits to buy. And the rabbits didn't say anything.

Pretty soon all the other animals returned tired, sunburned and thirsty. They looked for the Owl who had sold them the sandy, dusty, dry lands, and hoped to kill him slowly. But he had flown back to his cave in the hills.

So the beavers, skunks, woodchucks, foxes, bears, elephants and chickens started looking for the rabbits. "They must of known something," said an ocelot. "They laid off."

The only rabbit they could find was the one they thought was a coati-mundi. "Where's all the rabbits?" asked a mongoose.

"They've disguised themselves," testified the rabbit. "They all look like beavers and elks and geese and dogs and donkeys and butterflies and every other kind of animal. Next thing you know we'll all be intermarried and full of rabbit blood and full of elephant blood and tiger blood and mouse blood and dog blood and pigeon blood and every kind of blood just because them rabbits have fixed it so we don't know one from the other."

At this all the animals uttered cries of anguish. The big ones chased the little ones and the little ones chased each other because nobody knew who was who. There was a good deal of bloodshed so that blood could be inspected, and when everybody got tired of this, each animal retired to a separate university and started inventing bombs.

If anything came of it all it was the song which typified the period and the knowledge that rabbits cannot be trusted.

# THIS IS THE HUNT

Ominously

*mp*

This is the beast, the beast so sly, a

*mp*

no Pedal

murd-er-ous knave of bale-ful eye. These are the hunts-men,

brave and bold, boot-ed and spurred in the death-ly cold.

*less heavily and faster*

This is the maid - en, fine and frail, with

*less heavily and faster*

nob - le face and skin so pale. This is the Prince, so

*f rit.*

tall and strong, sworn to de-fend the right from wrong.

*mp a tempo*

These are the hounds, a - lert and a - ware,

keen - ly   snif - fing   the   dan - ger - ous   air.

Here   is   the   beast,   in   the   mid - night   hour,

*rit.*

steal - ing in stealth to the beau - ty's bow - er.

*rit.*

*mp a tempo*

Here is the Prince, on man - ly guard, pa -

*mp a tempo*

*mf*

trol - ling his post and breath - ing hard

*mp*

Here are the hounds, quick on the scent, wake - ful, a - watch, on

du - ty bent. Here is the maid - en, sweet - ly a - sleep,

start - led a - wake in the night so deep. Here is a scream,

full and round, heart - y and high, a helt' - ring sound.

Here goes the Prince with he - ro - ic bounds, and

here come the hunts-men and there go the hounds. And

there screams the maid, while there stands the fright,

caught in his e - vil, ringed by the light. Now

here is the hunt, and here is the chase.

# Wry Song

MANY ARE the stories, both true and untrue, told about Wolfo "Wenceslas" Binter, one of real Greats in the days of the early, or coffee grinder, school of ragtime piano playing. Tales are told about how at the age of two — 23 months to be exact — Maestro Binter went to the piano, an instrument he had never seen before, and picked out the note "A flat" with his little fist. Next he picked twenty-two cents in pennies out from between the keys.

These accomplishments behind him, young Wolfo retired from public performances except for a brief engagement in a revolving door at Belfazzer's Dept. Store at the age of three, which drew rave notices from the fire department. He was not seen again in any sort of starring role until in his seventh year he received a tool box for Big Sea Day and, while his elders were at the shore bathing, he sawed the piano apart, alone and unaided. His parents were so taken by this precociousness that they began locking him in the piano whenever they left to go visit a neighbor during the evening.

"It was more cultural and cheaper than a baby sitter," says Wolfo.

A significant incident occurred when his father and mother returned one evening with either Honus or Richard Wagner. Whichever it was, he was prevailed upon to play his latest opus and he immediately spent a half hour at the keyboard playing with both hands a good part of the time. Inasmuch as the notes sounded a little soggy, Mr. Wagner looked into the piano and discovered little Wolfo fast asleep (at least his eyes were closed). It is said that this performance made a lasting impression on the young Binter.

Upon being shaken awake Wolfo was observed to have a lump in his throat, and as a grateful gesture toward Mr. Wagner he sang in a childish tremolo (he was then but 32) the "Wry Song," which for sheer nuance is pretty hard to beat.

Binter, for some reason, retired shortly after this performance and was never seen out of his bed thereafter.

# WRY SONG

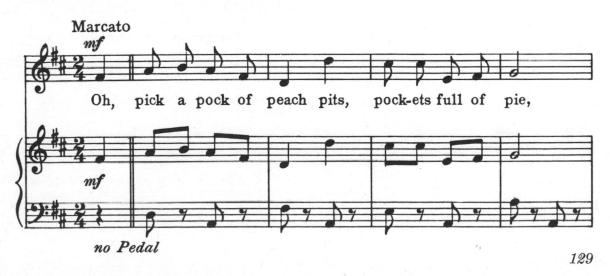

**Marcato**

Oh, pick a pock of peach pits, pock-ets full of pie,

*no Pedal*

Win-ni-peg was o - pen, the burst be-gan to sing. Oh,

worse than that a Dan-ish ditch was set be

*p rit.*

# *Potlucky*

AN INTERESTING story lies behind the rediscovery of the words to "Potlucky." The tune, of course, is the one which we all recognize.*

---

*All except Dr. Cubberd Nolt, who precipitated a prolonged argument at the historic July 3 meeting of the Birdsong Group with his flat statement, "I do not recognize that tune—nor any other tune." Dr. Nolt was relieved of his duties when it was pointed out that he should recognize the playing of "The Star Spangled Banner" because everybody stands up. His protest that this condition does not prevail in France was disallowed, and Dr. Nolt has retired to an embittered privacy in Nova Scotia. Rumor has it that the good doctor, practicing piano tuning in his spare time, has perfected the only piano in the Western Hemisphere tuned with 88 notes all in middle C. Further, it is believed that he has written a sonata for the instrument which contains an astonishing arrangement in the bass.

It must be admitted that Dr. Nolt has sent to the society a paper indicating that through his researches he has been able to demonstrate that not everyone does stand up when "The Star Spangled Banner" is played. His claim is that the piano player does not stand, the harpist remains seated, and Dr. Nolt's own father, Haynes, sort of crouches. Experts are of the opinion that old Mr. Nolt is a compulsive croucher and that this part of the findings indicates nothing. Dr. Nolt's other claims are being investigated under the terms of the Bundy Endowment. In the event that Dr. Nolt can indeed prove that he does not recognize even the National Anthem he will undoubtedly be reinstated and the society will be able to hear from the Doctor's own lips the story lying behind the words to "Potlucky."

# POTLUCKY

Briskly

1. Brisk - ly breath-ing Brack-ish brine Braz - en - ly we bray
2. Death - ly dump-lings Made of mud Grace our fest - ive board

mp non legato

no Pedal

Sim-mer-ing songs Of swim-ming swine Scat-ter-ing Sat - ur - day._
Free_ fro-men-ty! Flees the flood Fraught-ful fru-gal's floored.

Hearts are heav - y  Clubs are trump  Dia - monds are  in  rough
Hear ye! hear ye!  Hear ye! now!  Cup ye  now  an  eye

Spades are spot - ty  Jok - ers jump  Dum - mies are  e - nough.
Wea - ry, dea - rie  Ky - rie cow?  Moo and six  is  pie.___ The

Can we egg-plant?  Can we corn?  Can we suc-co-tash?
speak-er spokes The    real-er wheels A king-dom for a    hum  Oh,

String we strong-beans For the morn Mas-ter-ful (Tacet)    mus-tache?
rub - ba dub - ba    Dou-ble deals, Oh rub-ba dub (Tacet) - ba dub!

# *Willow the Wasp*

IN 1491 Bilbo Nortigger the Great Navigator gathered a small army and threatened to lay waste the summer palace of Emperor Klem I during the winter while it was unoccupied unless he was granted visas which would enable him to make his long-proposed trip around the world in order to prove his theory that the world was indeed round. As the Emperor was about to sign the necessary documents, word came through that Isabella had been seen entering a pawnshop in Lisbon.

"We must proceed with all possible haste!" exclaimed Nortigger. "The Queen has been approached by Christopher and they will attempt to prove the world is round before we do." Emperor Klem did his best, and in fourteen hours of hard, painstaking work, through the long hours of the night, he signed the three papers which Nortigger needed. One had to be returned and redone as Klem had signed his name incorrectly, using an "A" instead of an "E." As Bilbo was about to set sail he saw that another paper was signed with an "X," but was persuaded by Emperor Klem that this meant REX, Klem's first name.

Nortigger sailed due east. He claimed that this was the best route and it *was* pleasant as far as the Mediterranean went. At the end of the sea, Nortigger noticed that there was no way to continue. "We will have to go back and sail around Africa, or around the top of Russia," Bilbo said (quite shrewdly, as we now know). His first mate was all for sailing back west a couple of knots, turning around, getting a good start and seeing how far they might plough across land. This suggestion was turned down on the grounds that it might defile the holy lands. "Besides," said Nortigger, "it's very warm there at this time of the year."

Not much is known of Nortigger and his fellows after they finally turned westward. However it is believed that they made it as far as the Straits of Gibraltar. His great-grandniece in later years, hearing of her uncle's fame, wrote "Willow the Wasp" and dedicated it to the man who except for chance would now be hailed as the one who proved the world was round. In respect to a great intellect and a courageous spirit, then, we print the song here in its entirety.

# Willow the Wasp

Hauntingly
mp

There were some wasps in our town who, with their wond'-rous wives, They

no Pedal

suck-led at the bram-ble bush in search of love-ly lives; ____ And,

rit.

when they saw the bush was dry, quick, each and ev-'ry one, They

wrapped it well in wire barb to shield it from the sun.

# Prettily Preen

THIS AIR, taken from the aria "Ua mau ke ea o ka aina i ka pono," might be mistaken for a Polynesian war chant, which it actually is supposed to represent in the opera *Lava-Lava Laverock*. In point of fact Dr. Mander Pestle came back from the Pacific Islands with a recording of this selfsame tune after a harrowing experience in a Troik's nest.

Troiks, as we all know, are the large dancing bird of the islands, much studied by naturalists, and for years destroyed in large numbers, not for their feathers or meat but simply because they make such a fierce outcry upon the birth of a son.

The male and the female both sit on the egg* during the hatching season, so that when the little Troik† is born joy knows no bounds in the Troik household. The father Troik leaps high in the air and utters shrill screams, somewhat like a man selling watermelons. Following this he returns to earth and runs about telling all his friends, who are also overcome by joy and THEY run about telling their friends until every male Troik on the islands is running around telling some other Troik that another boy Troik has been hatched. Apparently female Troiks are never hatched, so that the Troik species is a very interesting crowd indeed.

Dr. Pestle in 1935 went out to the islands with nothing more than a handful of corn, glass beads (he thought the Troiks were pretty gullible, and moreover, he thought they were small), a suitcase containing clean socks and an early recording machine.

Pestle had been appointed by the Birdsong Group to record the caggle of the Troik. He approached his task with all the aids of modern science. The first afternoon in the islands he scaled a mound of several hundred feet and found the top was one huge Troik nest. Suitcase and recorder in hand, he stood on the edge of the nest peering in. Suddenly a huge shadow passed nearby and something swooped at him. Dr. Pestle had the presence of mind to quickly open his suitcase and pull it over his head. Something pounced upon him and poor Pestle found himself engulfed and trapped in his own suitcase.

Watchers from the shore said that a huge bird, a Troik, picked up Dr. Pestle in the suitcase, bore him to the nest and began to "set." It grew insufferably warm inside the suitcase, according to Dr. Pestle, and when all seemed quiet he stirred a bit, forced open the suitcase and climbed out. The Troik was lying in the corner of the nest, apparently intoxicated,‡ but he opened one eye and saw Dr. Pestle standing in the midst of twelve pairs of clean socks. The big bird leaped up, knocked over the recording machine, thus turning it on, and uttered many a loud cry of thanks and joy. Then the bird sprang into the air and flew off to tell his friends. Dr. Pestle grabbed the machine and ran for the boat. His companions rowed him swiftly to the steamer and the ship darted toward the horizon not a moment too soon. Back on the island the men could see that the utmost consternation was rife. Some speculated that the "father" was being derided for telling tall stories, some thought that the birds were forming a posse. At any rate Mander Pestle brought back to the Birdsong Group the cry of the Troik, although some researchers claim that the recording captured was lavishly§ larded with the cries of Dr. Pestle. However it is the best we have, and we rejoice in it.

---

*The egg is five feet square and resembles a suitcase. There is plenty of room for two.
†The little Troik is born weighing roughly the same, and standing roughly as tall as, say, Roughly Galento.

---

‡Try as they may, the editors have no explanation for this.
§If not completely.

# Prettily Preen

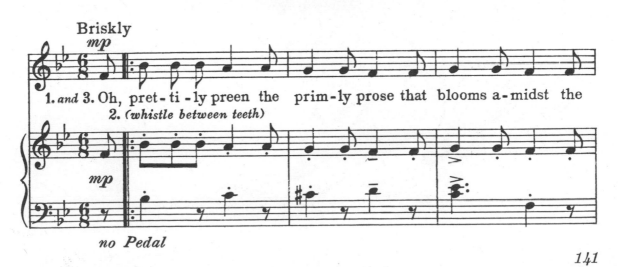

Briskly
*mp*

1. *and* 3. Oh, pret-ti-ly preen the prim-ly prose that blooms a-midst the
2. *(whistle between teeth)*

*mp*

no Pedal

Sun - day snows, And gloom the glib - ly gleam - ing glows while

subt-ly sup-ping sweet sup-pose. *(whistle between teeth)* 3. Oh sweet sup-pose.

# The Hazy Yon*

FOR MANY YEARS now in summer dells, evening grottoes and outdoor stadia throughout the country we have been treated to a revival of many fine old songs which might otherwise be dead. The parlor at home is enlivened these days with the gleaming television set, and scarcely one family in a thousand gathers around the old piano for a good family "sing." At very few gathering places for men, such as the locker room, salons, etc., do many of us burst into song. Therefore many of the songs of childhood go unsung; much of the music of yesterday is moldering away.

We can be thankful then to Miss Portlavoir DuPois, the singer of back-country songs, the hearty American girl with the untrained but magical voice. "It is like hearing angels," said Damrosch Pater. "*Lots* of angels." "Like the trump of Gabriel," said Mr. DuPois, her father. And who should know better? Miss DuPois is the one who revived the all but forgotten "The Hazy Yon."

"It is a song of gentle children gaily dancing and swinging through the trees on their way to the buttercups," Miss DuPois writes in her introduction to "Little Violets of April." "I remembered how when we were children we would gaily laugh and dance gaily as we went gaily out to pick buttercups, blueberries and other nosegays. Those were the happy hours and today it is a little different. Today, I, for one, cannot swing through the trees, and we have only the springtime of our summer memories as the autumn closes upon the winter of our mind, but the springtime follows when we hear the summer melodies and the autumn glows to a winter of tender thought."

It is in many ways unfortunate that this is the last song which we will have from the DuPois researches. Many of us will remember that in 1946 at the Mountain High Shell in Colorado Miss DuPois gave a memorable final farewell performance.

Seated on the flowered swing, Miss DuPois arched high over the assembled crowd out into the night, then back into the dazzling stage, then again gracefully out into the darkness over the canyon, then back. She had sung this most delightful of all children's swing songs quite a few times over and some of the crowd were growing a bit restive. Suddenly, as Miss DuPois, a large, well-rounded figure on a filmy swing, shot out of the lights into the darkness again, there was a report like a pistol shot,† and Miss DuPois was seen no more.

Listeners in the cheaper seats at the edge of the gulch said they heard Miss DuPois' voice fade away into nothing. There was a series of crashes on the beat (Miss Du Pois was an accomplished musician, though self-trained). And then there was stillness.

Observers reported later that it was the outstanding event of the season and it was a pity that it could not be repeated, but Miss DuPois was as good as her word. She never appeared again on any stage in this country. The broken and empty swing can be seen at the Mountain High Museum.

---

*Also known as "Carry Me Abacus To Old Abaddon."

†Some authorities state flatly that it WAS a pistol shot.

# THE HAZY YON

**Flowingly**

*mp*

How pierce - ful grows the  ha - zy  yon! How myr - tle  pet - aled

*with Pedal*

thou! _____ For spring hath sprung the  cy - clo - tron, How

high browse thou, brown cow?___ How high, how high browse

thou, browse thou, How high browse thou, brown cow?___ How

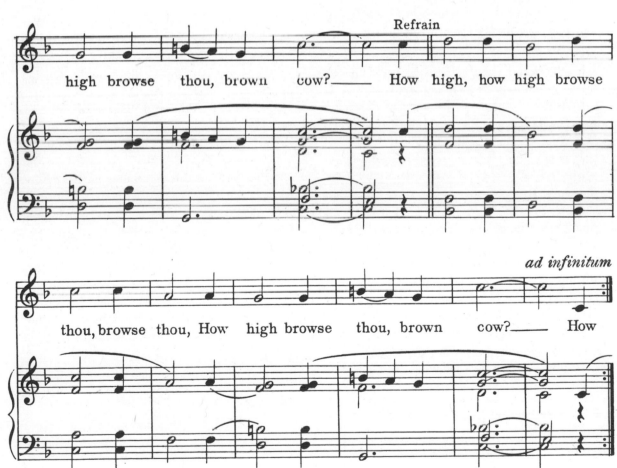

# Deck Us All With Boston Charlie

HERE IS an old and dearly loved carol, for many years mistakenly sung as "Deck the Halls With Boughs of Holly."* Generations of schoolboys have sung this song believing the latter title and corresponding words to be correct. Not to be outdone, generations of schoolgirls have known the carol as "Humm de humm humm humm dum dumhum."†

It is not difficult to picture how the original words (rediscovered and authenticated by Vairs Fresning) were twisted, as years went on, from their original meaning. Some authorities hold that there was at one time a comma between Boston and Charlie. It is true that Charlie is believed to have been told to stay away from Boston, or perhaps it was the other way around. However, the comma said to have been seen between Boston and Charlie is actually a comma regularly seen between Boston and Massachusetts by comma watchers everywhere.

Boston Charlie was believed‡ to have been a heroic figure during the Revolutionary War. When he performed a service for the British he was decorated with an eighteen-gun salute by the American troops, who sang in derision, "Decorate Us Too, With Boston Charlie."§ "Too" became "All" and "Decorate" was corrupted to "Deck" by a nearsighted naval officer.

The contention that the song was sung TO Charlie and should read " . . . with Boston, Charlie," is laughable and causes endless amusement whenever folklorists gather. It is rumored that there are some lost verses which have Charlie throwing a pie, known as a "Boston," at the small boys who gathered in front of his raffia shop. This theory is not quite in keeping with the facts, despite its obvious comedy. However, that is how many of our great songs have grown, and that is what makes trailing the elusive clue in folkwork so fascinating.‖

---

*This carol has also been confused with "Dicker Always Boss-man Holley," a political hymn of the early (6:15 A.M.) twenties.

†We may see here the root of "Home, Home on the Range."

‡Believed by Mrs. Boston Charlie, that is.

§"With" actually meant "alongwith." The tax on letters prevented use of the longer word. — Basnil's *Authority*.

‖Myriad Blemish, in her "Tea Cozies and Sea Chanteys," describes her adventures while accidentally locked into a carpenter shop, where she built a creditable dog house. "The reward of the search is often more than we expect," says Miss Blemish.**

**Very true, too.

# Boston Charlie

Gaily

*mf*

Deck us all with Bos-ton Char-lie, Wal-la Wal-la, Wash., an'

*mf*

*no Pedal*

Don't we know ar - cha - ic bar - rel, Lul - la - by Lil - la Boy,

Lou - is - ville Lou. Trol - ley Mol - ly don't love Har - old,

boo - la  boo - la  Pen - sa - coo - la    hul - la - ba - loo!

# INDEX OF FIRST LINES

## ABOUT WALT KELLY

*WALT KELLY was born in Philadelphia just a few months ahead of the World Series of 1913 (Philadelphia Athletics, 4 games to the N. Y. Giants' 1). Encouraged by this, he waited two years and left for Bridgeport, Connecticut, taking his mother, father, sister and a large bag of animal crackers.*

*This latter influence started him on the right road, and after fooling around with school into his sixteenth year he became a newspaper cartoonist, a newspaper reporter and then an animator at Disney studios in Burbank, California. He returned to the United States in 1941 in search of food; spent some time in the foreign language unit of the Armed Forces Institute (much to his surprise and that of his superiors); invented Pogo for comic-book use; graduated him to a newspaper comic strip in 1948 in the New York Star. Seeking to fill the daily strips with easy material, he wrote a number of nonsense verses. Editors were too stunned by these to protest quickly enough and so they were printed. This book is a collection of that material. It shows what can happen when 450 newspaper editors are not alert.*

## ABOUT NORMAN MONATH

*NORMAN MONATH was born, according to his own account, in Canada several years ago, but he doesn't say how many. By 1941 he was old enough at least to graduate from N.Y.U. as a music major. The major became a sergeant in the Second World War and composed the official song of the Rainbow (42nd) Division. General Harry J. Collins gave him a decoration for this feat, although, again, Monath doesn't say what or where. Other compositions include chamber music of various kinds, children's songs for Golden Records and popular songs recorded by Burl Ives, Kaye Ballard and Percy Faith, just to drop a few names. Mr. Monath's career took a mysterious twist in 1954 when he invented the card word game called Bali. He is co-author of a book of games entitled* Play It Yourself *which is published by Pocket Books, Inc. About himself Norman says, "Now live quietly (don't know what this really means) with my wife in the village (Greenwich)."*

*Well, his wife, Pauline (fine woman, brunette, pretty), knows what it means. She says, "He plays the piano and sings his own compositions while I keep praying out loud that he gets a chance to do a musical." Call that quiet? Hah!*